Really Easy Guitar!

Christmas Hits

KT-555-292

Wise Publications
London/New York/Paris/Sydney/
Copenhagen/Madrid/Tokyo

Contents

Exclusive distributors:
Music Sales Limited
8/9 Frith Street, London W1D 3JB, England.
Music Sales Pty Limited
120 Rothschild Avenue, Rosebery, NSW 2018,
Australia.

Order No. AM971564
ISBN 0-7119-8994-X
This book © Copyright 2001
by Wise Publications

Written, compiled and arranged by Joe Bennett
Edited by Sorcha Armstrong
Music processed by The Pitts and Paul Ewers

CD mastered by Kester Sims
Tracks programmed by John Moores
and Paul Honey
All guitars by Arthur Dick

Book design by Chloë Alexander
Artist photographs courtesy of LFI
Introduction photographs by George Taylor

Printed in the United Kingdom by
Printwise (Haverhill) Limited, Haverhill, Suffolk.

Introduction

Welcome to Really Easy Guitar, a fantastic new way to learn the songs you love.

This book will teach you how to play 14 classic songs – and you don't even have to be able to read music!

Inside you will find lyrics and chords for each song, complete with the chord shapes you need to start playing immediately. There's a special introduction to each song, with helpful hints and playing tips. Fretboxes and guitar TAB teach you the famous riffs and patterns that everyone will recognise. The accompanying 15-track CD features professionally recorded soundalike versions of each song, for you to sing along to.

Just follow the simple four-step guide to using this book and you will be ready to play and sing along with your favourite Christmas classics!

1 Tune Your Guitar

Before you can start to play along with the backing tracks, you'll need to  make sure that your guitar is in tune with the CD. Track 1 on the CD gives you notes to tune to for each string, starting with the bottom E string, and then working upwards.

Alternatively, tune the bottom string first and then tune all the other strings to it.

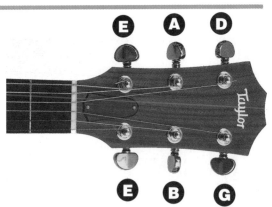

Follow the tuning diagram below and tune from the bottom string upwards.

6th to 5th string   5th to 4th string   4th to 3rd string   3rd to 2nd string   2nd to 1st string

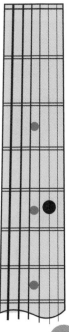

2 Understanding fretbox diagrams

Throughout this book, fretbox diagrams are used to show chord shapes and scale patterns. Think of the box as a view of the fretboard from head on – the thickest (lowest) string is on the left and the thinnest (highest) string is on the right.

The horizontal lines correspond to the frets on your guitar; the circles indicate where you should place your fingers.

An x above the box indicates that that string should not be played; an o indicates that the string should be played open.

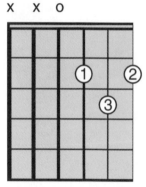

Hence, when playing this chord of D, make sure that you don't hit the bottom two strings.

All the chords you need for each song are given at the top of the song, in the order that they appear in that song.

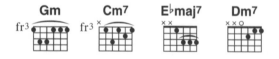

Shapes that are played higher up the neck are described in the same way – the lowest fret used is indicated to the left of the box. A curved line above the box shows that a first finger barre should be used.

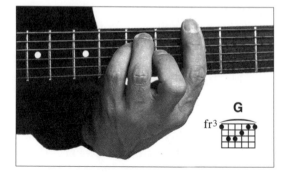

This barre chord of G is played at the third fret, with the first finger stretching across all six strings.

3 Understanding scale patterns

We can also use chord box diagrams to show you certain useful scale patterns on the fretboard. When a box is used to describe a scale pattern, suggested fingerings are also included.

Black circles show you the root note of the scale. If the root note of the scale is an open string, this is indicated by a double circle. Grey circles represent notes of the scale below the lowest root note.

So in this example, the root note of the scale is the open D string, with another D appearing at the third fret on the B string.

4 Understanding TAB

TAB is another easy way to learn the famous riffs and hooks in each song. The six horizontal lines represent the six strings of the guitar – the lowest line represents the lowest string (low E), while the highest line represents the highest string (high E). The number on each line tells you which fret should be played.

Although we've also included traditional music notation, you don't actually need to be able to read music to use TAB – just listen to the recording and follow the fret positions on the TAB and you'll soon be playing along. There are certain special symbols which are used:

Hammer-on

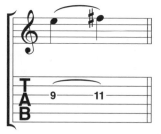

Look out for a slur connecting two numbers – when the second number is higher than the first this is called a "hammer-on". Place one finger at the lower of the two frets indicated and pick that string, then, without picking the string again, place your next finger at the higher fret. You should hear a smooth change in sound between the two notes.

Pull-off

A pull-off is the opposite of a hammer-on, and is denoted by a slur joining two TAB numbers, where the second number is lower than the first one.

Place your fingers at the two fret positions indicated, and pick the first (higher) note, then simply lift the top finger, without picking the string again, allowing the bottom note to ring out.

Slide

A slide between two notes is denoted by a short line in the TAB. Simply play the first note, and then move your finger to the new fret position by sliding it along the fretboard, restriking the string as you arrive at the new position.

Legato slide

A legato slide is exactly the same as a normal slide, except that the second note is not picked again.

Bend

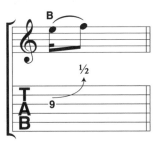

String bends are indicated as shown above – the amount that you need to bend the string is indicated near the arrow and could be ¼ tone (a decorative bend), ½ tone (the equivalent of one fret) or 1 tone (the equivalent of two frets).

Palm Muting

To get this percussive effect, place the side of your picking hand against the strings near the bridge as you pick.

Chris De Burgh

THIS UNUSUAL TAKE on the Christmas story was released in 1986 as a double A side with the ballad 'The Ballroom of Romance'. Although it only reached number 40 in the UK charts at the time, Chris de Burgh's catchy 'la la la la' chorus has made it an annual favourite ever since.

▼ E Natural Minor Scale

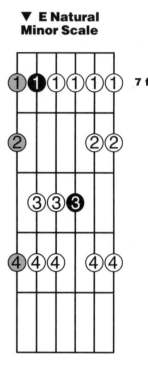

7 fr

How to play it
The original recording is in the key of D minor, but for our CD version we've transposed it into the key of E minor to make the chords easier. The most difficult chord is the Bm because it features a partial barre – apply even pressure with the flattened first finger of the fretting hand, and make sure each note sounds clearly throughout.

Guitar part
On the original recording, the electric piano carries most of the harmony. To create a playable guitar part, you could use strumming, single-note picking or ideally a mixture of both. Try to include dynamics where you can – the chorus' guitar part should be noticeably louder than the verse's.

Melody notes
If you want to have a go at playing the melody, all of the notes are taken from the E natural minor scale (see fretbox). You may also want to try using these notes to improvise your own melodic lines over the CD backing track.

Guitar sound
Chris uses an Ovation 12-string when he performs live, but any acoustic guitar should sound fine. If you're playing the song on electric, use a clean tone, and if possible add compression, chorus and reverb to the basic guitar sound.

▼ A Spaceman Came Travelling – chorus melody

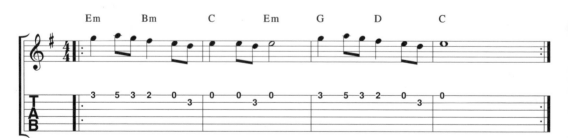

Chris De Burgh

2 A Spaceman Came Travelling

Words & Music by Chris De Burgh

Em   D   C   G   Bm

Intro | Em D | C Em | G D | C | C D | Em | Em ||

Verse 1
```
      Em              G                D          Em
A spaceman came travelling on his ship from afar,
      G           D                C               D
'Twas light years of time since his mission did start.
      Em   Bm      C           Em
And over a village he halted his craft
      G           D            C          D  Em
And it hung in the sky like a star, just like a   star.
```

Verse 2
```
      Em         G              D         Em
He followed a light and came down to a shed
      G           D                 C                D
Where a mother and child were lying there on a bed,
      Em              Bm   C              Em
A bright light of silver shone round his head
      G          D          C             D         Em
And he had the face of an angel and they were afraid.
```

Verse 3
```
          Em          G     D            Em
Then the stranger spoke, he said "Do not fear,
      G           D       C                       D
I come from a planet a long way from here
      Em      Bm            C               Em
And I bring a message for mankind to hear."
      G           D       C            D  Em
And suddenly the sweetest music filled the air.
```

Chorus 1

```
     C D    Em    Bm    C      Em
And it went, la la la, la la la, la la la, la,
G        D      C D Em   Bm    C      Em
La la la, la la la, la   la la la, la la la, la la la, la,
G          D          C          D           Em      C  D
Peace and good will to all men and love for the child.
Em      Bm    C     Em
La la la, la la la, la la la, la,
G        D      C D Em   Bm    C      Em
La la la, la la la, la   la la la, la la la, la la la, la,
G        D      C   Em
La la la, la la la, la.
```

Verse 4

```
      Em      G        D              Em
This lovely music went trembling through the ground
      G        D          C                  D
And many were wakened on hearing that sound,
      Em          Bm     C        Em
And travellers on the road the village they found
      G          D          C           D  Em
By the light of that ship in the sky which shone a - round.
```

Verse 5

```
      Em        G      D         Em
And just before dawn at the paling of the sky
      G      D              C              D
The stranger returned and said "Now I must fly.
          Em          Bm        C            Em
When two thousand years of your time have gone by
      G         D     C         D  Em
The song will begin once again to a baby's cry."
```

Chorus 2   As Chorus 1

Outro   *Spoken over Chorus*

Oh the whole world is waiting, waiting to hear that song again,

There are thousands standing on the edge of the world

And a star is moving somewhere, the time is nearly here,

This song will begin once again to a baby's cry.

3 Fairytale Of New York

The Pogues

THIS 1987 NUMBER 2 HIT features Pogues singer Shane MacGowan and the late Kirsty MacColl. It takes the form of a drunken Christmas Day argument between an Irish couple, talking about their times in New York City. There is an unconfirmed but popular rumour that notorious drinker MacGowan was actually drunk when they recorded it.

How to play it
The song begins with a very slow feel on piano and strings. If you play guitar for this section, use clean, clear down-strums for each chord. The Irish folk rhythm picks up in the first instrumental, just after the Gsus4 chord. Even if you are only strumming once every beat, note that there are some difficult sections here – the C F G C bar is particularly difficult because you're changing chord each time you strum.

Rhythm part
The song is in 12/8 time, which means, in guitar terms, that you should count four to the bar, but each count is divided up into three – count "one-and-a-two-and-a-three-and-a-four-and-a". The easiest way to play rhythm guitar along with the CD is simply to strum four downstrokes per bar, but try throwing in a few upstrokes to vary the part if possible. The acoustic guitar part on the recording is arpeggiated – i.e. the plectrum picks out single notes of each chord. This is fairly rapid picking, so make sure you can play the song comfortably with strumming before you try arpeggio picking.

Guitar sound
This is Irish folk music, so you really should be playing acoustic guitar here. A true folkie will have heavy bronze or phosphor strings fitted – 13 or 14 gauge ideally – but you'll manage OK with a lighter set as long as you don't pick the notes too heavily.

▼ **Fairytale Of New York – easy picking pattern**

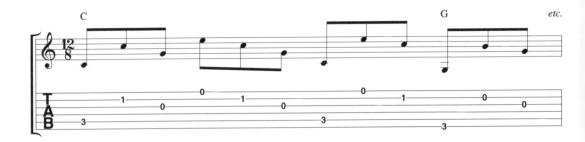

Shane MacGowan
(The Pogues)

3 Fairytale Of New York

Words & Music by Shane MacGowan & Jem Finer

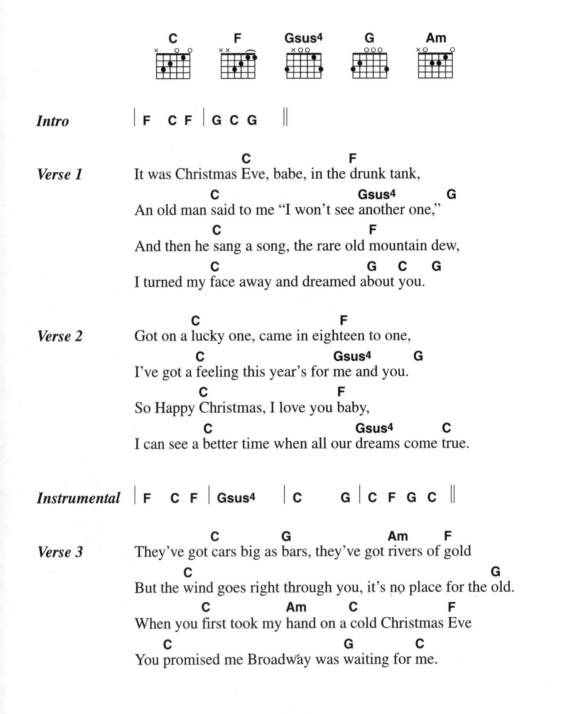

Intro
| F C F | G C G ||

Verse 1

                        C   F
It was Christmas Eve, babe, in the drunk tank,
                C   Gsus4   G
An old man said to me "I won't see another one,"
               C   F
And then he sang a song, the rare old mountain dew,
               C   G   C   G
I turned my face away and dreamed about you.

Verse 2

              C   F
Got on a lucky one, came in eighteen to one,
              C   Gsus4   G
I've got a feeling this year's for me and you.
             C   F
So Happy Christmas, I love you baby,
              C   Gsus4   C
I can see a better time when all our dreams come true.

Instrumental
| F C F | Gsus4 | C   G | C F G C ||

Verse 3

              C   G   Am   F
They've got cars big as bars, they've got rivers of gold
             C   G
But the wind goes right through you, it's no place for the old.
             C   Am   C   F
When you first took my hand on a cold Christmas Eve
             C   G   C
You promised me Broadway was waiting for me.

Verse 4

              C   G

You were handsome, you were pretty, queen of New York City.

         C   F   G   C

When the band finished playing, they howled out for more.

    C   G

Sinatra was swinging, all the drunks they were singing,

     C   F   G   C

We kissed on a corner then danced through the night.

Chorus 1

                   F   Am G   C   Am

And the boys from the NYPD   choir were singin' 'Galway Bay'

        C   F   G   C

And the bells were ringin' out for Christmas Day.

Link 1

‖ C G Am F ‖ C   G ‖ C Am C F ‖ C   G C ‖

Verse 5

              C   G

You're a bum, you're a punk, you're an old slut on a junk

        C   F   G   C

Lying there almost dead on a drip in that bed.

    C   G

You scumbag, you maggot, you cheap lousy faggot,

     C   F   G   C

Happy Christmas your arse, I pray God it's our last.

Chorus 2   As Chorus 1

Link 2   ‖ C   ‖ F   ‖ C   F ‖ G C G   ‖

Verse 6

             C   F

I could have been someone, well so could anyone.

             C   Gsus4   G

You took my dreams from me when I first found you.

             C   F

I kept them with me, babe, I put them with my own,

               C   F   G   C

I can't make it   all alone, I've built my dreams around you.

Chorus 3   As Chorus 1

4 Frosty The Snowman

THIS CHRISTMAS CLASSIC has been recorded over 100 times in the last century, with jazz and blues luminaries such as Jimmy Durante, Fats Domino and Ella Fitzgerald, as well as more recent pop acts such as the Jackson Five and even the Cocteau Twins. Our version is a lively pop recording, with a few of those essential jazz chord changes included just to keep things interesting!

How to play it

The song is actually in the key of F, but this makes it extremely difficult to play on guitar, so we've written out the chords in the key of D. Simply use a capo at the third fret if you're going to play along to the CD. Don't be put off by those bizarre chord names like G♯ dim (G sharp diminished) – many of them are no more difficult than regular chords. Check the fretboxes and you'll see that the three diminished chords are actually the same four-string chord shape, with the whole shape simply moved up or down the neck.

Chord changes

What makes the song challenging to play is not the chords themselves but the speed at which they change. In these sections (e.g. "with a corncob pipe and a button nose…") try playing each chord as a single down-strum, giving you more time to change to the next one. Note also that the track has a very full arrangement on its backing track. This means the rhythm guitar doesn't need to work especially hard in order to fill out the sound. So if you're having difficulty with a particular chord change, try playing fewer notes of the current chord (e.g. just the three thinnest strings) and simply ignoring the other notes with the fretting and picking hand.

Rhythm part

Because the song is at a fairly fast tempo, you can choose to use rhythmic strumming (up-down-up-down, or any rhythmic pattern that sounds good) or – as on the recording – single-note picking. Here, the electric guitar part picks out single notes of the current chord and plays them one at a time. It doesn't matter which notes you pick, as long as they are actually part of the current chord.

Guitar sound

The recorded guitar part uses a chorus and tremolo effect, and a single-coil pickup type guitar, with compression and reverb added. An electric guitar will usually sound better if you're choosing to try single-note picking, but you may prefer an acoustic if you play the song as fully strummed chords.

▼ **D major scale shape**

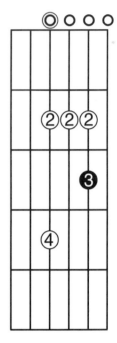

'Fats' Domino

4 Frosty The Snowman

Words & Music by Steve Nelson & Jack Rollins

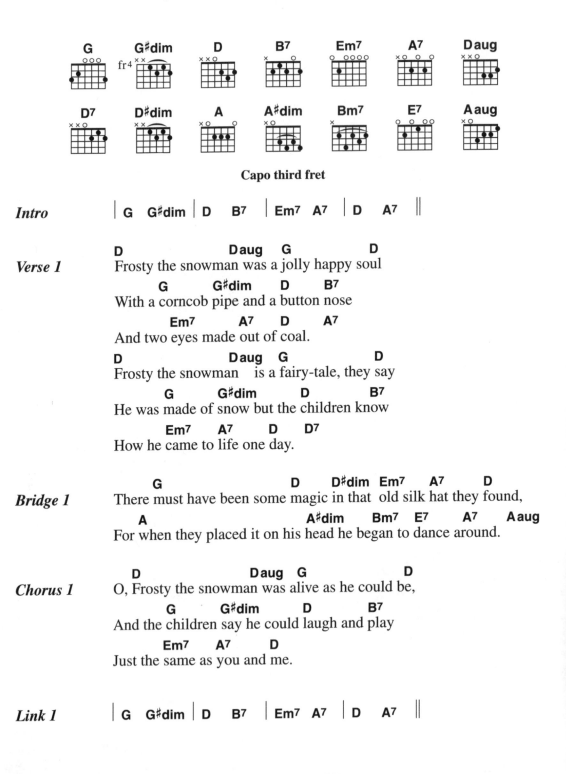

Capo third fret

Intro
| G   G♯dim | D   B7 | Em7   A7 | D   A7 ‖

Verse 1
```
        D                  Daug   G              D
Frosty the snowman was a jolly happy soul
        G       G♯dim     D     B7
With a corncob pipe and a button nose
        Em7       A7    D    A7
And two eyes made out of coal.
D                    Daug   G              D
Frosty the snowman   is a fairy-tale, they say
        G       G♯dim      D         B7
He was made of snow but the children know
        Em7     A7      D     D7
How he came to life one day.
```

Bridge 1
```
        G                     D     D♯dim Em7    A7       D
There must have been some magic in that  old silk hat they found,
    A                      A♯dim    Bm7  E7     A7     Aaug
For when they placed it on his head he began to dance around.
```

Chorus 1
```
        D                 Daug  G            D
O, Frosty the snowman was alive as he could be,
        G        G♯dim      D        B7
And the children say he could laugh and play
        Em7     A7      D
Just the same as you and me.
```

Link 1
| G   G♯dim | D   B7 | Em7   A7 | D   A7 ‖

Verse 2

   D   Daug   G   D
Frosty the snowman knew the sun was hot that day,
      G   G♯dim   D   B7
So he said "Let's run and we'll have some fun now
     Em7 A7   D   A7
Before I melt away."
   D   Daug   G   D
Down to the village with a broomstick in his hand,
      G   G♯dim   D   B7
Running here and there, all around the square,
      Em7   A7   D   D7
Saying "Catch me if you can".

Bridge 2

     G   D   D♯dim   Em7 A7   D
He led them down the streets of town right to the traffic cop,
    A   A♯dim   Bm7   E7   A7   Aaug
And he only paused a moment when he heard him holler "Stop!"

Chorus 2

   D   Daug   G   D
For Frosty the snowman had to hurry on his way,
      G   G♯dim   D   B7
But he waved goodbye saying "Don't you cry,
   Em7   A7   D   D7
I'll be back again some day."

Bridge 3

     G   D   D♯dim Em7   A7   D
There must have been some magic in that old silk hat they found,
    A   A♯dim   Bm7 E7   A7   Aaug
For when they placed it on his head he began to dance around.

Chorus 3

   D   Daug G   D
O, Frosty the snowman was alive as he could be,
      G   G♯dim   D   B7
And the children say he could laugh and play
      Em7   A7   D
Just the same as you and me.

Link 2

| G G♯dim | D   B7 |

Outro

     Em7 A7   D
I'll be back again some day.

| Em7 A | D   ‖

19

5 Happy Xmas (War Is Over)

John Lennon

ALTHOUGH JOHN LENNON'S Christmas classic was first released as early as 1971, it found its greatest success in the three years after his death in 1980. It has charted a total of five times – more than any Beatles song or solo Beatle recording.

How to play it
Hearing the simple main chord riff (see tab below), you can imagine John writing the song, sitting there with 6-string acoustic. Play an A chord, take one finger off, put another finger on, then go back to the A chord. Sounds great – until you then try to do the same thing with the Bm and E chords. It's much more difficult to get the chords sounding clearly when you're holding down a barre shape, and the stretch required to get that Eadd9 chord is just painful. Try doing the whole thing while strumming rapid up-and-down strokes, and it's time to put your fingers in traction. It is just about possible to get by playing only the first chord of every line (e.g. just staying on A or B♭ for the whole phrase) but if you put in the extra effort to manage the changes the results are worth it. So if you want authenticity, you've got no alternative but to learn those shapes.

The strumming hand doesn't get off lightly either. Keep that down down-up down-up rhythm going throughout, counting "one two-and-three-and" as you strum. You should hold the plectrum as lightly as you can without dropping it, and strum with the elbow and wrist as relaxed as possible.

Guitar sound
The original recording uses 6- and 12-string acoustic guitars, all playing the same strumming part, while another guitar plays mandolin-style rapid picking along with the main chord riff. The song always sounds better on an acoustic 12-string, but bear in mind that this will make the chord changes more difficult – particularly the Bm in the second line.

▼ Happy Xmas (War Is Over) – main chord riff in A

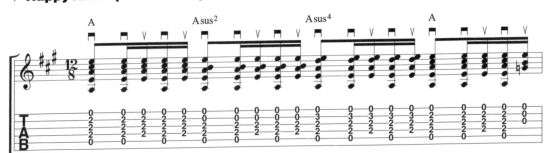

WAR IS OVER!
IF YOU WANT IT

John Lennon and Yoko Ono

Happy Christmas from John & Yoko

5 Happy Xmas (War Is Over)

Words & Music by John Lennon & Yoko Ono

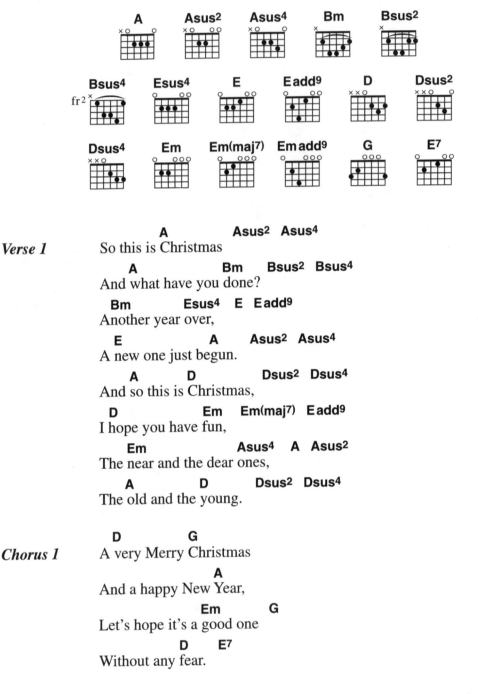

Verse 1

         A   Asus2 Asus4
So this is Christmas

     A   Bm   Bsus2 Bsus4
And what have you done?

 Bm   Esus4 E Eadd9
Another year over,

   E   A   Asus2 Asus4
A new one just begun.

    A   D   Dsus2 Dsus4
And so this is Christmas,

    D   Em   Em(maj7) Eadd9
I hope you have fun,

    Em   Asus4 A Asus2
The near and the dear ones,

   A   D   Dsus2 Dsus4
The old and the young.

Chorus 1

   D   G
A very Merry Christmas

        A
And a happy New Year,

       Em   G
Let's hope it's a good one

      D   E7
Without any fear.

Verse 2

              A   **Asus2 Asus4**
And so this is Christmas

      A   **Bm**   **Bsus2 Bsus4**
For weak and for strong,

    Bm   **Esus4**   **E Eadd9**
The rich and the poor ones,

      E   **A**   **Asus2 Asus4**
The road is so long.

      E   **D**   **Dsus2 Dsus4**
And so happy Christmas

     D   **Em**   **Em(maj7) Eadd9**
For black and for white,

     Em   **Asus4**   **A Asus2**
For the yellow and the red ones,

    A   **D**   **Dsus2 Dsus4**
Let's stop all the fights.

Chorus 2   As Chorus 1

Verse 3

              A   **Asus2 Asus4**
And so this is Christmas

      A   **Bm**   **Bsus2 Bsus4**
And what have we done?

    Bm   **Esus4** **E Eadd9**
Another year over,

     E   **A**   **Asus2 Asus4**
A new one just begun.

     A   **D**   **Dsus2 Dsus4**
And so happy Christmas,

    D   **Em** **Em(maj7) Eadd9**
I hope you have fun,

     Em   **Asus4**   **A Asus2**
The near and the dear ones,

    A   **D**   **Dsus2 Dsus4**
The old and the young.

Chorus 3   As Chorus 1

Outro

A   **Asus2**   **Asus4**   **A**
War is   o   -   ver,

Bm   **Bsus2**   **Bsus4** **Bm**
If   you   want   it,

Esus4   **E**   **Eadd9**   **E**   **A**   **Asus2 Asus4 A**
War   is   o -   ver now.

Happy Christmas.

6 I Believe In Father Christmas

Greg Lake

GREG LAKE TOOK a brief break from '70s prog-rock superstars Emerson, Lake and Palmer to record this 1975 single. Its video (or 'promotional film' as they were called back then) was actually shot in the desert, presumably to remind people that the real meaning of Christmas has nothing to do with snow and everything to do with the Middle East!

How to play it
The song opens with a fiendishly difficult finger-picked part which continues throughout (we've given you the first three bars of the intro below). To make things easier, we've used similar chord shapes in the fretboxes, but these can be picked or strummed as you choose, depending on your level of experience. The song originally used 'dropped D' tuning (i.e. loosen the bass E string until it's tuned to a note of D). You can try this for yourself – simply retune the string, and then whenever you see a D chord in the music, strum all six strings instead of just four.

Note that almost all of the chords in the song are either D chords or end in /D (meaning that you should play D in the bass). This is called a pedal note and this is what gives the song its carol-like, heavenly sound. To play this on a guitar, Greg Lake plays a note of D with the thumb in between every chord he plucks with the fingers. You can try this for yourself – pluck the three thinnest strings with your first, second and third fingers, and then play the open D note with the thumb in the gaps. You can do this throughout the track, apart from the two A7 chords right at the very end.

Guitar sound
If you're playing 6-string acoustic, use the thickest strings your fingers can stand, and dispense with the plectrum, even if it feels uncomfortable at first. Electric guitar players could try adding chorus and reverb to a clean guitar sound, but the real key to getting the sound right here is getting used to that off-beat thumb pedal technique.

▼ Guitar fingerpicking intro (first 3 bars)

Greg Lake

6 I Believe In Father Christmas

Words & Music by Greg Lake & Peter Sinfield

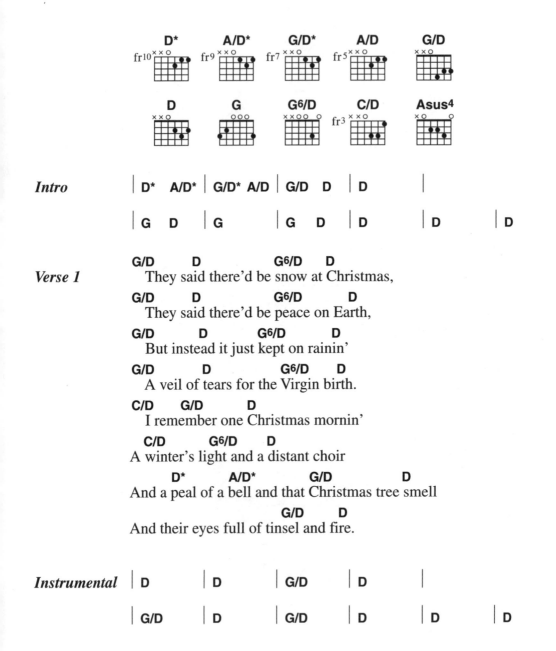

Intro

| D* A/D* | G/D* A/D | G/D D | D | |

| G D | G | G D | D | D | D |

Verse 1

G/D   D   G6/D   D
   They said there'd be snow at Christmas,

G/D   D   G6/D   D
   They said there'd be peace on Earth,

G/D   D   G6/D   D
   But instead it just kept on rainin'

G/D   D   G6/D   D
   A veil of tears for the Virgin birth.

C/D   G/D   D
   I remember one Christmas mornin'

C/D   G6/D   D
A winter's light and a distant choir

     D*   A/D*   G/D   D
And a peal of a bell and that Christmas tree smell

             G/D   D
And their eyes full of tinsel and fire.

Instrumental

| D | D | G/D | D | |

| G/D | D | G/D | D | D | D |

Verse 2

```
G/D       D        G6/D       D
```
They sold me a dream of Christmas,
```
G/D       D        G6/D       D
```
They sold me a silent night,
```
G/D          D          G6/D   D
```
And they told me a fairy story
```
G/D          D                G6/D    D
```
Till I believed in the Israelite.
```
C/D           G/D     D
```
And I believed in Father Christmas
```
       C/D           G6/D     D
```
And I looked to the sky with excited eyes,
```
        D*           A/D*        G/D        D
```
Then I woke with a yawn in the first light of dawn
```
                  C/D          D
```
And I saw him and blew his disguise.

Instrumental

| D | D | G/D | D | |
| G/D | D | G/D | D | D | D | |

Verse 3

```
G/D   D         G6/D       D
```
I wish you a hopeful Christmas,
```
G/D   D         G6/D           D
```
I wish you a brave New Year,
```
G/D       D   G6/D       D
```
All anguish, pain and sadness
```
G/D          D               G6/D      D
```
Leave your heart; and let your road be clear.
```
C/D       G/D             D
```
They said there'd be snow at Christmas,
```
   C/D   G6/D           D
```
They said there'd be peace on Earth,
```
    D*       A/D*     G/D        D
```
Hallelujah Noel, be in Heaven or Hell,
```
                G6/D        D
```
The Christmas we get, we deserve.

Instrumental

| D | D | G/D | D | |
| G/D | D | G/D Asus4 | D | Asus4 | D | |

7 I Wish It Could Be Christmas Every Day

Wizzard

THIS SONG REAPPEARS every year, and you'll find it on many a Christmas compilation. It was recorded in 1973 by Roy Wood's band Wizzard, and features the essential Christmas song elements of sleigh bells and children's choir, combined with the glam-rock sounds of saxophone, electric guitar and shuffle beat drums.

How to play it
Wait for eight clicks, then simply strum the D chord in an even, relaxed down-up movement in time with the snare drum. Keep this rhythmic pattern going throughout the main parts of the song, but try to play the same rhythm as the saxophone in the middle and at the end of each chorus.

Just before each chorus, there's a rapid three-chord change over the words "Well I wish…". Practise this section separately before you play along to the CD, because the fast movement is much more difficult than the one-chord per bar changes in the rest of the song.

The instrumental section is fairly straightforward, but it does feature a time-signature change just before the sax solo. This is marked N.C. (no chord) in the tab. Be ready to pick up that Bm strum in time when the saxophone comes in.

Guitar sound
Roy Wood was famous for appearing with mad-looking guitars, but the actual sound on 'I Wish It Could Be Christmas Every Day' is actually a fairly straightforward clean electric guitar tone. If you wish, you could add a little bit of overdrive/distortion from your amp, but keep this to a minimum so that the chords still ring out clearly. Select the bridge pickup and add some reverb from the amp if you have it. If you're playing this song on acoustic, now's the time to get a thick plectrum, and strum as strongly as you can using up and downstrokes – let the chords strum out for Christmas!

▼ Intro and Strumming Pattern

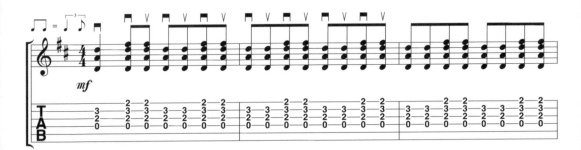

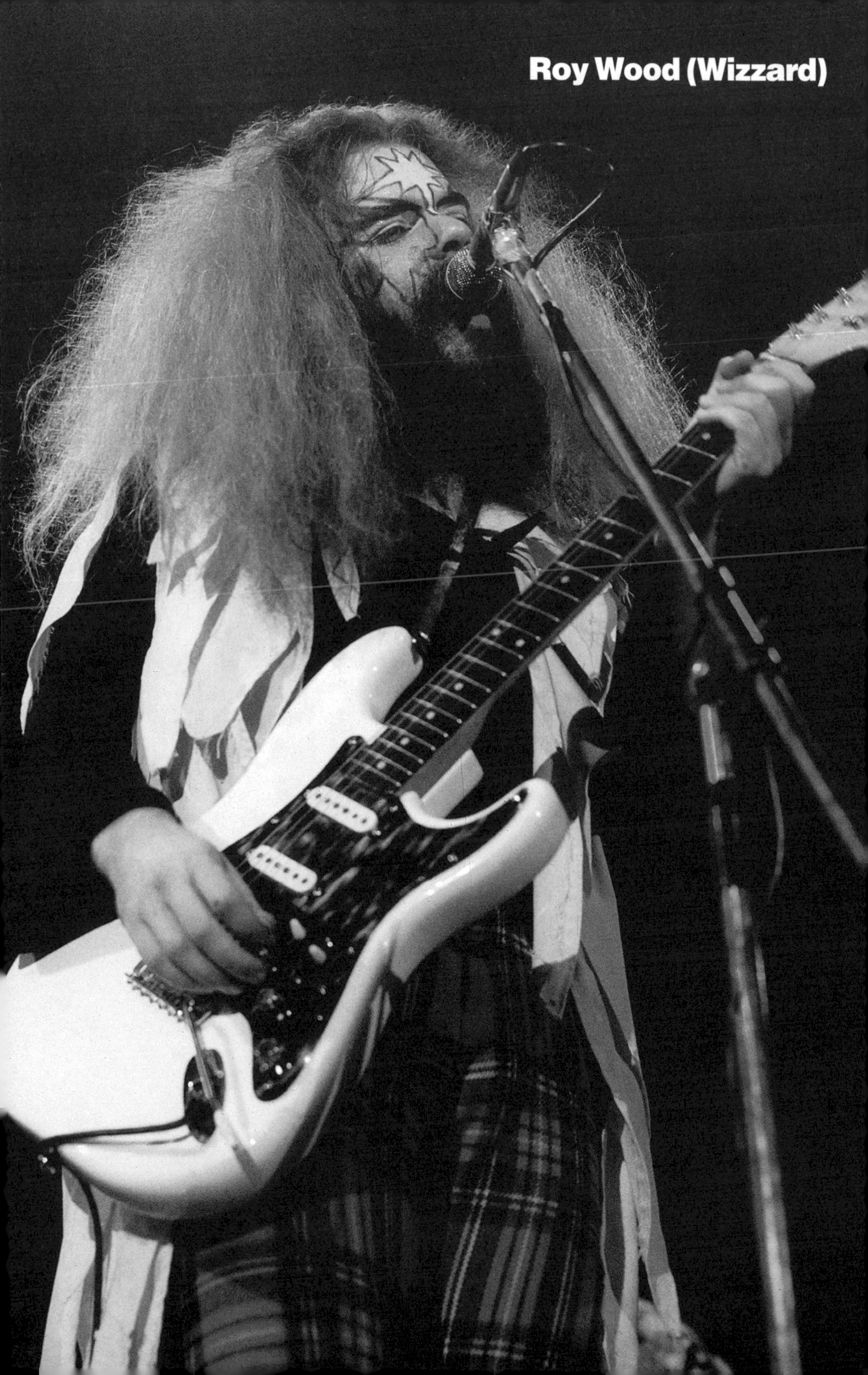
Roy Wood (Wizzard)

I Wish It Could Be Christmas Every Day

Words & Music by Roy Wood

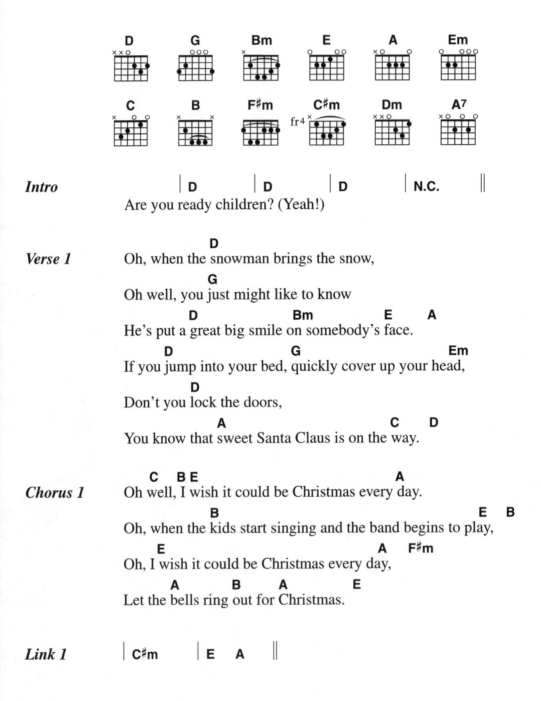

Intro | D | D | D | N.C. ||

Are you ready children? (Yeah!)

Verse 1

              D
Oh, when the snowman brings the snow,

           G
Oh well, you just might like to know

       D   **Bm**   **E**   **A**
He's put a great big smile on somebody's face.

     D   **G**   **Em**
If you jump into your bed, quickly cover up your head,

       D
Don't you lock the doors,

       A   **C**   **D**
You know that sweet Santa Claus is on the way.

Chorus 1

       C **B E**   **A**
Oh well, I wish it could be Christmas every day.

         B   **E** **B**
Oh, when the kids start singing and the band begins to play,

   E   **A** **F#m**
Oh, I wish it could be Christmas every day,

     A   **B**   **A**   **E**
Let the bells ring out for Christmas.

Link 1 | C#m | E   A ||

Verse 2

              D   G
When we're skating in the park, if the snow cloud paints it dark,

              D   Bm   E   A
Then your rosy cheek's gonna light my merry way.

              D   G   Em
Now the frosticles appear and they've frozen up my beard,

              D   A   C   D
So we'll lie by the fire 'til the sleep simply melts 'em all away.

Chorus 2

           C   B E   A
Oh well, I wish it could be Christmas every day.

               B   E   B
Oh, when the kids start singing and the band begins to play,

    E   A   F#m
Oh, I wish it could be Christmas every day,

     A   B   A
Let the bells ring out for Christmas.

Instrumental | N.C. | N.C. | Bm | E | A | A | Bm | Dm |

| A | A | D | D | G | G | A⁷ | A⁷ ||

Verse 3

                   D
Oh, when the snowman brings the snow

(When the snowman brings the snow)

            G
Well you just might like to know (well he just might like to know)

              D   Bm   E   A
He's put a great big smile on somebody's face.

            D
So if Santa brings our sleigh (Santa brings that sleigh)

            G   Em
All along the Milky Way (along the Milky Way),

              D   A   C   D
I'll sign my name on the roof in the snow, then he may decide to stay.

Chorus 3   As Chorus 1

Okay you lot, take it!

Chorus 4   As Chorus 2

    F#m   A   B   A   E
Outro   Why don't you give your love for Christmas?

8 In Dulci Jubilo

Mike Oldfield

IT'S NOT OFTEN that you hear a Christmas single that's almost 400 years old, purely instrumental, and 50% guitar solo, but back in 1975 this is what Mike Oldfield released. The original melody is by JS Bach, adapted by Oldfield, and features recorder player Leslie Penning playing the main theme.

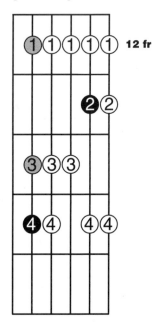

▼ **C Major Scale (12th fret position)**

12 fr

How to play it
We've shown the chords for the whole track in the fretboxes, but let's face it – with an instrumental as famous as this, everyone wants to have a go at the tune! In the tab over the page you'll find a transcription of the main recorder melody, specially adapted for easy guitar. Anchor your first finger at the 5th fret, using your second finger for any notes that appear at the 6th, the third for the 7th, and the little finger for the 8th fret. This is called 'position playing' and is the key to achieving speed in lead guitar parts. Near the end of the tune, you have to move out of position for one note – slide your first finger back to the 4th fret, then along again to the 5th to put you back in position for the last phrase.

Rhythm part
If you do want to have a go at strumming the chords, listen to the acoustic guitar part at the very start of the track. Note that the part uses an 'oom-pah' style accompaniment, where the bass note is picked followed by the chord. You can do this with plectrum or fingers, but plectrum is recommended because it's likely to give a stronger rhythmic feel.

Solo
The fast guitar solo uses the 12th fret position C major scale (see fretbox). Once you've taught your fingers to play these notes (see if you can do it without looking at the fretbox or fingerboard) try making up melodies using any notes of the scale. You can start improvising right from the beginning of the track, even over the top of the recorder melody.

Guitar sound
Most Mike Oldfield recordings from this era (even a version of the Blue Peter theme, which he recorded in the late 1970s) feature the same lead guitar sound. It's a smooth heavily overdriven tone created by using an electric guitar with a humbucking pickup into a valve amplifier. Most modern amps will recreate this fairly accurately simply by increasing the 'gain' or 'drive' levels, though some players may find that they need to select the neck pickup, and possibly turn down the treble control, in order to get that smooth, thick sound. Add subtle reverb and play as cleanly and accurately as you can.

Mike Oldfield

In Dulci Jubilo

Composed by Johann Sebastian Bach
Arranged by Mike Oldfield

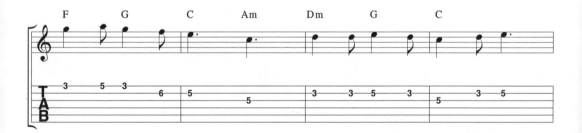

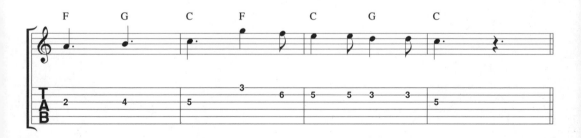

▼ **Chord shapes for**

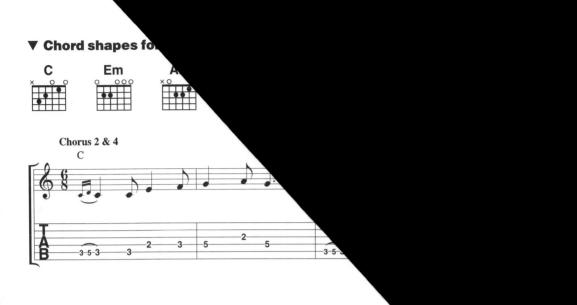

C **Em** **A**

Chorus 2 & 4

C

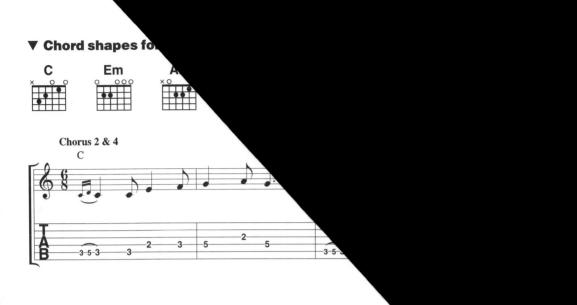

Em   Am   Dm   G

F   G   C   Am   Dm   G   C

F   G   C   F   C   G   C

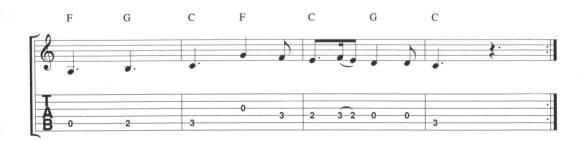

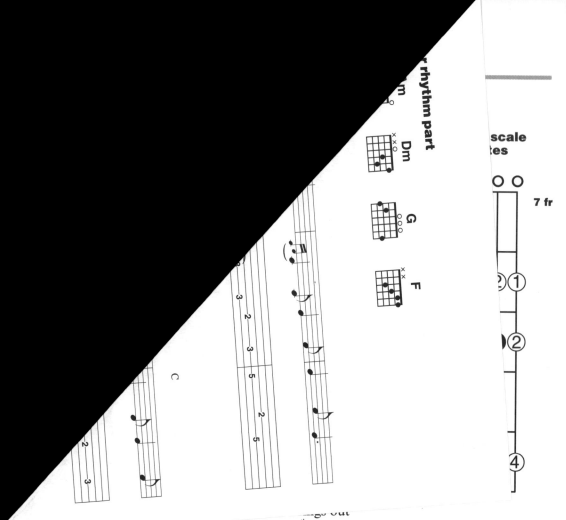

...practise changing to and from the F#m from the chords either side (i.e. E to F#m to B7).

Guitar sound

Any sound should be fine here as long as you don't use distortion for electric guitar parts, as this will get in the way of the clarity of the chords. If you're playing acoustic, strum directly over the soundhole with a lively down-up motion. Electric guitarists may find they get a better sound just playing the off-beat chords. If you want to use effects, compression, chorus and subtle reverb should be all you need.

Bing Crosby

Traditional

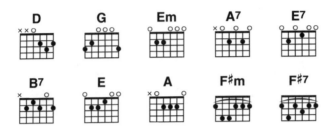

Capo first fret

Intro **Sleigh bells for 4 bars**

Chorus 1

D   G   D
Jingle bells, jingle bells, jingle all the way,

Em   A7   D   E7   A7
Oh what fun it is to ride in a one-horse open sleigh.

D   G   D
Jingle bells, jingle bells, jingle all the way,

Em   A7   D   A7   D
Oh what fun it is to ride in a one-horse open sleigh.

Link 1 | N.C. | N.C. | N.C. | N.C. ||

Verse 1

D   G
Dashing through the snow in a one-horse open sleigh,

Em   A7   D
O'er the fields we go, laughing all the way.

                                        G   B7
Bells on bob-tail ring, making spirits bright,

         Em   A   A7   D
What fun it is to ride and sing a sleighing song tonight.

Chorus 2

D   G   D
Jingle bells, jingle bells, jingle all the way,

Em   A⁷   D   E⁷   A⁷
Oh what fun it is to ride in a one-horse open sleigh.

D   G   D
Jingle bells, jingle bells, jingle all the way,

Em   A⁷   D   A⁷   D
Oh what fun it is to ride in a one-horse open sleigh.

Link 2

| N.C. | N.C. | N.C. | N.C. ‖

Verse 2

D   G
Now the ground is white, go it while you're young,

Em   A⁷   D
Take the girls tonight, sing this sleighing song.

                                                      G   B⁷
Get a bob-tailed bay, two-forty for his speed,

         Em   A   A⁷   D
Then hitch him to an open sleigh and you will take the lead.

Chorus 3

D   G   D
Jingle bells, jingle bells, jingle all the way,

Em   A⁷   D   E⁷   A⁷
Oh what fun it is to ride in a one-horse open sleigh.

D   G   D
Jingle bells, jingle bells, jingle all the way,

Em   A⁷   D   A⁷   D
Oh what fun it is to ride in a one-horse open sleigh.

Chorus 4

E   A   E
Jingle bells, jingle bells, jingle all the way,

F♯m   B⁷   E   F♯⁷   B⁷
Oh what fun it is to ride in a one-horse open sleigh.

E   A   E
Jingle bells, jingle bells, jingle all the way,

F♯m   B⁷   E   B⁷   E F♯m B E
Oh what fun it is to ride in a one-horse open sleigh.

10 Lonely This Christmas

Mud

'LONELY THIS CHRISTMAS' was one of three No. 1 hits for Mud, reaching the top of the chart in December 1974. Its Elvis-tribute vocal was apparently done in the studio as a joke, but the band liked it so much that it stayed on the final recording.

How to play it
The song consists almost entirely of four chords, played over and over – G, Em, C and D. On the recording these chords are actually B♭, Gm, E♭ and F, but because many less experienced players find these shapes quite painful, we've shown the song in the key of G. Put a capo on at the 3rd fret and play the chords as shown in the fretboxes when you play along to the CD.

Rhythm part
The guitar part on the original (and our soundalike version) is a typical 1950s ballad off-beat – the guitar plays one very short chord on beat two and four of each bar. The arpeggios suggest that the backing chords are played by a harp on the CD, but you could try them on guitar simply by playing each chord in the style shown in the tab below. Pick one note at a time with the plectrum, and let each string ring on for as long as possible until the next chord change.

Guitar sound
If you're playing the off-beat single strum part, use a very bright, trebly guitar sound, and select the bridge pickup. A little reverb should enhance the sound and add to that retro ballad feel. If you decide to try the arpeggio part shown in the tab, this should work fine on electric or acoustic guitar – again, add reverb if you have it.

▼ Easy guitar fingerpicking excerpt

10 Lonely This Christmas

Words & Music by Mike Chapman & Nicky Chinn

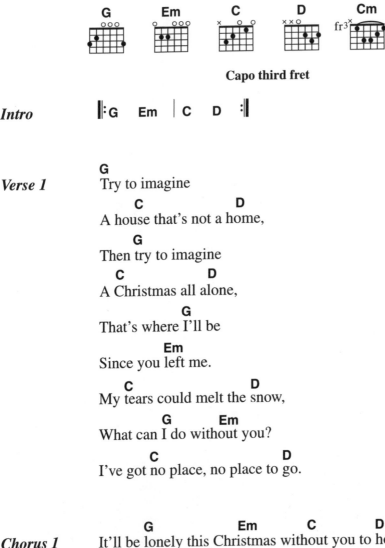

Capo third fret

Intro   ‖: G   Em | C   D :‖

Verse 1
G
Try to imagine
    C   D
A house that's not a home,
    G
Then try to imagine
    C   D
A Christmas all alone,
              G
That's where I'll be
          Em
Since you left me.
    C   D
My tears could melt the snow,
        G   Em
What can I do without you?
    C   D
I've got no place, no place to go.

Chorus 1
        G   Em   C   D
It'll be lonely this Christmas without you to hold,
        G   Em   C   D
It'll be lonely this Christmas, lonely and cold.
        G   Em   C   D
It'll be cold, so cold, without you to hold
        G   C G D
This Christmas.

Verse 2

G
Each time I remember

    C   D
The day you went away,

        G
And how I wouldn't listen

    C   D
To the things you had to say.

     G   Em
I just break down as I look around

      C   D
And the only things I see

   G   Em
Are emptiness and loneliness

     C   D
And an unlit Christmas Tree.

Chorus 2

      G   Em   C   D
It'll be lonely this Christmas without you to hold,

      G   Em   C   D
It'll be lonely this Christmas, lonely and cold.

      G   Em   C   D
It'll be cold, so cold, without you to hold

    G   C G D
This Christmas.

Chorus 3

      G   Em   C   D
It'll be lonely this Christmas without you to hold,

      G   Em   C   D
It'll be lonely this Christmas, lonely and cold.

      G   Em   C   D
It'll be cold, so cold, without you to hold

    G   C Cm G
This Christmas.

Outro
(Spoken)

Merry Christmas darling, wherever you are.

Slade

'MERRY XMAS EVERYBODY' is, without a doubt, the most famous rock Christmas single of all time. It went straight to No. 1 when it was released on 15 December 1973, selling over 1 million copies in the UK. It's since been released as a UK single another seven times, and features on just about every Christmas party album you can buy.

How to play it
Although the song is mainly in the key of G, what makes it interesting for a guitarist is the B♭ chord that crops up in the intro and chorus. In the fretbox we've shown the 'rock' B♭ chord shape favoured by guitarists Noddy Holder and Dave Hill. You can play this using all four fingers, or the easy way using the first finger at the first fret, and the little finger flattened across the D, G and B strings at the third fret. Make sure you don't play either of the outer two strings.

If you find the intro (see tab below) too difficult, feel free to leave this section out and let the CD take over – on the original recording the guitars don't come in until the verse anyway.

For the other chord shapes in the song, we've shown the easiest version of each in the fretboxes. If you know a barre chord version of G, Em, Bm and D, feel free to use these. Whichever you try, make sure you concentrate mainly on the bass notes of each chord to keep the accompaniment going.

Guitar sound
To play this one properly, you're going to need an electric guitar and some sort of distortion sound – i.e. a pedal or an amp with a gain control. Turn up the drive or gain setting fairly high (around 50%) and back off the treble slightly on the amp. The guitar's volume should be set at full and the bridge pickup selected. There is added reverb on the original recording, but no other effects are used.

▼ **Merry Xmas Everybody – intro (transcribed for guitar)**

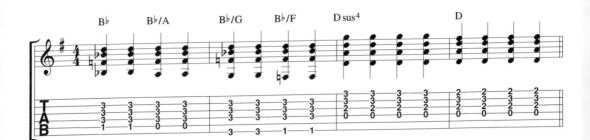

**Noddy Holder
(Slade)**

11 Merry Xmas Everybody

Words & Music by Neville Holder & James Lea

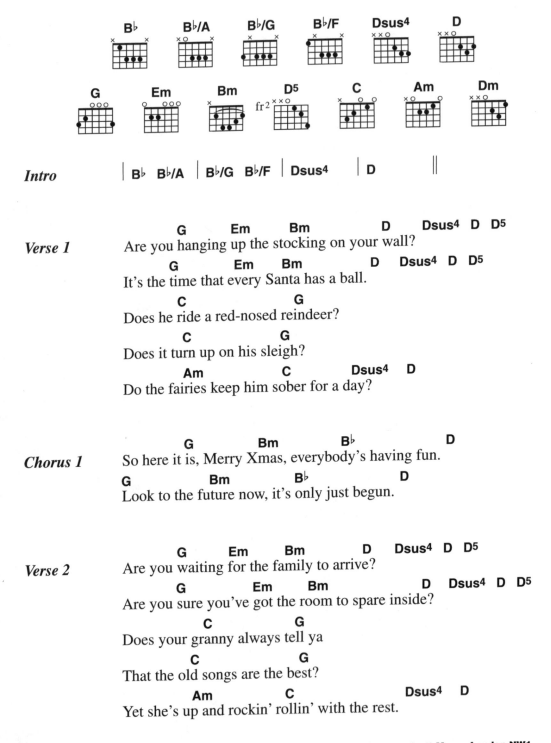

Intro | Bb Bb/A | Bb/G Bb/F | Dsus4 | D ‖

Verse 1

       G   Em   Bm   D   Dsus4 D D5
Are you hanging up the stocking on your wall?
       G   Em   Bm   D   Dsus4 D D5
It's the time that every Santa has a ball.
     C   G
Does he ride a red-nosed reindeer?
     C   G
Does it turn up on his sleigh?
    Am   C   Dsus4   D
Do the fairies keep him sober for a day?

Chorus 1

       G   Bm   Bb   D
So here it is, Merry Xmas, everybody's having fun.
G   Bm   Bb   D
Look to the future now, it's only just begun.

Verse 2

       G   Em   Bm   D   Dsus4 D D5
Are you waiting for the family to arrive?
       G   Em   Bm   D   Dsus4 D D5
Are you sure you've got the room to spare inside?
     C   G
Does your granny always tell ya
     C   G
That the old songs are the best?
    Am   C   Dsus4   D
Yet she's up and rockin' rollin' with the rest.

Chorus 2

         G   **Bm**   **B♭**   **D**
So here it is, Merry Xmas, everybody's having fun.
G   **Bm**   **B♭**   **D**
Look to the future now, it's only just begun.

Bridge

Dm   **B♭**
What will your daddy do

                   Dm
When he sees your mother

         B♭   **C** **D**
Kissing Santa Claus? Ah ha…

Verse 3

        G   **Em**   **Bm**   **D**   **Dsus4** **D** **D5**
Are you hanging up your stocking on the wall?
        G   **Em**   **Bm**   **D**   **Dsus4** **D** **D5**
Are you hoping that the snow will start to fall?
    C   **G**
Do you slide up and down the hillside
    C   **G**
In a buggy you have made?
          Am   **C**   **Dsus4**   **D**
When you land upon your head then you've bin' slayed!

Chorus 3

         G   **Bm**   **B♭**   **D**
‖: So here it is, Merry Xmas, everybody's having fun.
G   **Bm**   **B♭**   **D**
Look to the future now, it's only just begun.
        G   **Bm**   **B♭**   **D**
So here it is, Merry Xmas, everybody's having fun.
G   **Bm**   **B♭**   **D**
Look to the future now, it's only just begun. :‖

12 Mistletoe And Wine

Cliff Richard

THIS SENTIMENTAL BALLAD, which was a Christmas number 1 in 1988, was actually originally recorded by Twiggy before it was a hit for Sir Cliff Richard. It's a great piece for guitarists for two reasons – firstly the original recording doesn't feature any guitar, so you can make up your own part, and secondly it features six really easy chords.

How to play it
Wait for the end of the tinkling glockenspiel/chimes intro, then come in with a single down-strum of C at the start of verse 1. Keep the guitar part simple to begin with – as the song builds you'll need some room to get more complex towards the end. You can play the accompaniment as strums, picked arpeggio notes, or a mixture of both.

Arpeggio picking part
To create an arpeggio part, fret the chords as normal and pick the strings one at a time with the plectrum, starting with the bass note of the current chord (in the case of a C chord, this would be a note of C at the third fret of the A string). Then pick the three thinnest strings one at a time in one direction, then back again, and repeat. If you pick evenly in time with the accompaniment, you'll end up back where you started in time for the next bar of music.

Instrumental
The instrumental section is simply a repeat of the chorus, but you may wish to strum more firmly and rhythmically for this section, to maintain the same feel as the band as the dynamics lift.

Guitar sound
If you're using electric guitar, try to get as close to the chiming effect of the keyboard part as you can. For this you'll need a bright guitar sound (use the bridge pickup, with the volume and tone controls up full on your guitar) and perhaps a chorus effect. Add plenty of reverb (set to 'Hall' if you have the facility) and pick delicately at the start, getting gradually louder as the track progresses. An acoustic guitar will usually sound better playing a strummed part, but if you want to try picked arpeggios, make sure each fretted note sounds clearly without any fret buzz.

Mistletoe and time
The song is in a 3/4 (waltz) time signature, meaning that some strumming patterns you may use on other songs won't work as well here. To help you keep time, try counting three-to-the-bar in time with the music. If this is difficult at first, simply use three even down strums for each bar. After that, try varying the rhythm pattern to incorporate upstrokes too. A typical acoustic guitar rhythm could be Down Down-Up-Down-Up, or just Down Down-Up Down.

Cliff Richard

12 Mistletoe And Wine

Words by Leslie Stewart & Jeremy Paul
Music by Keith Strachan

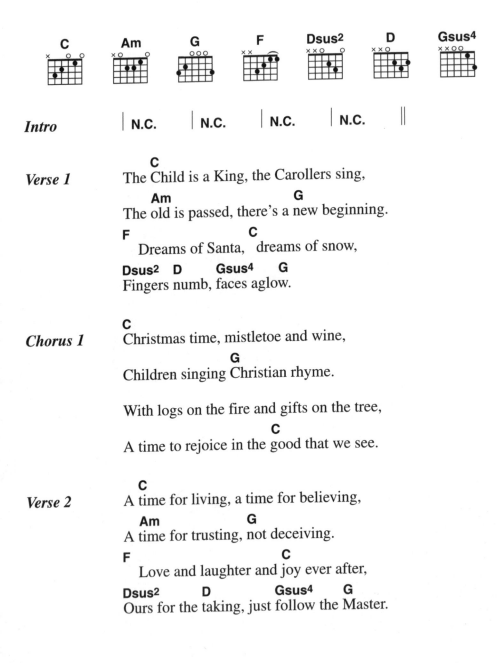

C   Am   G   F   Dsus2   D   Gsus4

Intro
| N.C. | N.C. | N.C. | N.C. ||

Verse 1

    C
The Child is a King, the Carollers sing,

  Am   G
The old is passed, there's a new beginning.

F   C
  Dreams of Santa, dreams of snow,

Dsus2 D   Gsus4   G
Fingers numb, faces aglow.

Chorus 1

   C
Christmas time, mistletoe and wine,

              G
Children singing Christian rhyme.

With logs on the fire and gifts on the tree,

                  C
A time to rejoice in the good that we see.

Verse 2

   C
A time for living, a time for believing,

  Am   G
A time for trusting, not deceiving.

F   C
  Love and laughter and joy ever after,

Dsus2   D   Gsus4   G
Ours for the taking, just follow the Master.

Chorus 2

    C
Christmas time, mistletoe and wine,

           G
Children singing Christian rhyme.

With logs on the fire and gifts on the tree,

              C
A time to rejoice in the good that we see.

Verse 3

    C
A time for giving, a time for getting,

    Am   **G**
A time for forgiving and forgetting.

F   **C**
Christmas is love, Christmas is peace,

Dsus2   **D**   **Gsus4**   **G**
A time for hating and fighting to cease.

Chorus 3

    C
Christmas time, mistletoe and wine,

           G
Children singing Christian rhyme.

With logs on the fire and gifts on the tree,

              C
A time to rejoice in the good that we see.

Chorus 4

    C
Christmas time, misletoe and wine,

           G
Children singing Christian rhyme.

With logs on the fire and gifts on the tree,

              C
A time to rejoice in the good that we see.

Elton John

ELTON JOHN'S 1973 SINGLE is one of the few examples of a Christmas song featuring a really solid acoustic guitar riff (see tab). Although it only got to No. 24 in the charts at the time, it still reappears every December, and its up-tempo rock feel has made it many a guitarist's favourite Christmas song.

How to play it
Because all the guitars on the original recording are acoustic, the whole guitar part stays around simple open chord shapes wherever possible – which is great news for beginner guitarists! Even the main riff (see tab) is mostly based on three single strums of a D chord. To keep the lively rhythmic feel going, use up- and down-strokes wherever possible, being careful not to catch unwanted bass strings on some chords (e.g. make sure that every time you play a D chord you only hit four strings).

Rhythm part
With this kind of rock acoustic rhythm guitar, you need to pivot from the elbow rather than the wrist, strumming up and downstrokes with the same even motion. The trick here is to avoid gripping the plectrum too tightly as this will restrict rhythmic movement. This strumming style continues right up until the instrumental section (around 2:10 on your CD) – note that at this point the chords are arpeggiated – i.e. picked one at a time.

Guitar sound
Bronze-strung acoustic is really the only authentic instrument to use, but if you only have an electric guitar, select a middle pickup position, set your amp up 'flat' (i.e. with all tone controls at 12 o'clock) and use a clean guitar tone with very little reverb.

▼ **Step Into Christmas – acoustic guitar riff**

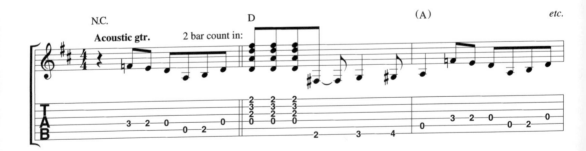

13 Step Into Christmas

Words & Music by Elton John & Bernie Taupin

Intro ‖: D | A | D | A :‖

Verse 1

D
Welcome to my Christmas song,
G   **D**
   I'd like to thank you for the year,

So I'm sending you this Christmas carol,
G   **D**
   To say it's nice to have you here.

Am   **G**
   I'd like to sing about all the things
  D   **A**
Your eyes and mind can see,
Am   **G**
   So hop around your turntable
Em   **A**
   Oh, step into Christmas with me.

Chorus 1

D
Step into Christmas, let's join together,
   G   **A**
We can watch the snow fall forever and ever.
D
Eat, drink and be merry, come along with me,
G   **E7**   **A Asus4 A**
   Step into Christmas,   the admission's free.

Verse 2

      D
Take care in all you do next year,
  G   **D**
  You keep smiling through the days,

If we can help you, entertain you,
  G   **D**
  Oh ho, we will find a way.

    Am   **G**
So merry Christmas one   and all,
        D   **A**
There's no place I'd rather be
Am   **G**
But asking you if you'll oblige,
Em   **A**   **Asus⁴** **A**
Steppin' into Christmas with me.

Chorus 2

  D
Step into Christmas, let's join together,
    G   **A**
We can watch the snow fall forever and ever.
D
Eat, drink and be merry, come along with me,
G   **E⁷**   **A** **Asus⁴** **A**
  Step into Christmas,   the admission's free.

Instrumental | D | G | A | D | Bm | E | A | A

               | D | A | D | A | D | A | D | A |

Verse 3   As Verse 1

Chorus 3   ‖: As Chorus 1 :‖ *Repeat to fade*

14 Winter Wonderland

IT'S RARE TO HEAR a Christmas song that is also a 'jazz standard', but the jazzy changes and swing beat of 'Winter Wonderland' are unmistakable. Jazz giants such as Louis Armstrong, Chet Baker and Ella Fitzgerald have all recorded this tune, along with slightly more predictable Christmas crooners like Dean Martin and Tony Bennett. It's a challenge for a guitarist because of its use of diminished and 11th chords, not to mention a few tricky half-bar changes.

How to play it
Our jazz-band version uses electric piano, bass and drums, and leaves off the guitar part, giving you plenty of room to add your own ideas. The simplest way to play along is to strum a single downstroke for each chord change and let it ring on. This is fine while you're getting to know the chords, but hopefully you'll want to develop something more adventurous.

Strumming pattern
Once the more difficult shapes (A♯dim, C♯, G♯ and B11) are comfortably under your fingers, try playing four downstrokes to the bar, strumming the top (thinnest) few strings only. These are called partial chords, and are an essential element of jazz rhythm guitar (they're also easier than regular chords!). The first example of a half-bar change occurs at the end of the first chorus, when you need to play B7, then E7, then A. Practise this section separately before you try to incorporate it into the rest of the song. When you've mastered it, do the same with the more difficult C♯-G♯-C♯ change from the middle section.

Guitar sound
The classic electric guitar jazz sound uses the neck pickup, a semi-solid 'f-hole' guitar, and the tone turned to about half on the guitar, with no other effects used. Solid-bodied electric guitars can be made to approximate this tone by using the same settings but also turning down the treble control on the amp. However, if you find this sound is just too muddy for your taste, try using a more straightforward clean guitar sound with a chorus effect – this will go well with the electric piano on the CD recording.

Tough chords?
If you still find those new chords too difficult, here are a few tips on playing them quickly and easily. Take a look at the A♯dim chord. Notice how the top three strings (the thinnest) are similar to an open chord of D7? This means that if you only play those 3 notes, you don't have to play the tricky half-barre behind the A♯dim.

If you're having trouble with the B11, apply the same principle. Note that it shares the notes on the D, G and B strings with a regular chord of A. This means that if you play those notes of an ordinary A chord along with the backing track, the resulting 'partial' chord will sound good as part of the song.

Frank Sinatra, Bing Crosby
and Dean Martin

14 Winter Wonderland

Words by Richard Smith
Music by Felix Bernard

Capo first fret

Intro ‖ E | E | B7 E | A ‖

Verse 1

              A   A#dim
Sleigh bells ring, are you listening?
     E7
In the lane snow is glistening.

A beautiful sight, we're happy tonight
B7   E7   A
Walking in a winter wonderland.

Verse 2

          A   A#dim
Gone away is the bluebird,
       E7
Here to stay is a new bird.

He sings a love song, as we go along,
B7   E7   A
Walking in a winter wonderland.

Bridge 1

C#   G#   C#
In the meadow we can build a snowman,
C#   G#   C#
Then pretend that he is Parson Brown.
E   B11   E
He'll say "Are you married?" We'll say "No, man"
   F#7   B7   E7
But you can do the job when you're in town.

Verse 3

       A   A#dim
Later on we'll conspire
        E7
As we dream by the fire,

To face unafraid the plans that we made
B7   E7   A
Walking in a winter wonderland.

Verse 4   As Verse 1

Verse 5   As Verse 2

Bridge 2

C#   G#   C#
In the meadow we can build a snowman
C#   G#   C#
And pretend that he's a circus clown.
E   B11   E
We'll have lots of fun with Mister Snowman
    F#7   B7   E7
Until the other kiddies knock him down.

Verse 6

       A   A#dim
When it snows, ain't it thrilling?
        E7
Though your nose gets a chilling.

We'll frolic and play the Eskimo way,
B7   E7   A   E
Walking in a winter wonderland,
B7   E7   A
Walking in a winter wonderland.

15 Wonderful Christmastime

Paul Mc Cartney

JUST AFTER THE break-up of Wings, Paul McCartney released this synthy Christmas song in time for the 1979 Christmas top 10. Because the song was written on a keyboard, it's actually much easier to play on synthesiser than guitar, so we've shown slightly simplified chords for guitarists, using a capo at the 3rd fret.

How to play it
First of all, put your capo on or you'll be out of tune with the backing track. The verse consists of four chords – Gmaj7, G6, D/G and then G. Even though the chord names may not be familiar to some players, check out the fretboxes and you'll see that they are actually all variations on a normal G chord. On the original recording, the synth plays these chords through an echo device. On guitar, you could strum a single chord and let it ring, or use gradually lighter downstrokes to simulate the echo effect.

Chorus
The chorus is by far the most difficult part of the song to play on guitar, not because of the chords themselves, but because they change on every single beat. Note that the music shows an F7 chord. Use this shape if you are comfortable with it, but if you find it too difficult at this speed, replace it with a regular F chord, which many people find slightly easier.

Guitar sound
Any clean guitar sound should work here, whether on electric or acoustic guitar, but you may wish to try a chorus effect to fit with the chiming sound of the CD track. If you want to be really clever you could actually use the same echo setting as the original. Set up a delay effect, with the mix at around 50%, 20-30% feedback, and a delay time of 310ms, and then play each chord once only along with the keyboard part on the CD. The echoes will be exactly in time with the music. Hey, it beats learning to play keyboards!

▼ Wonderful Christmastime – chorus melody

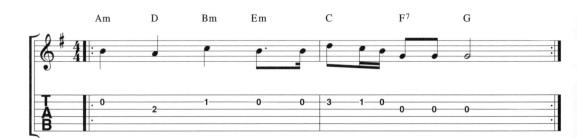

Paul Mc Cartney

15 Wonderful Christmastime

Words & Music by Paul McCartney

Gmaj7   G6   D/G   G   Am

D   Bm   Em   C   F7

Capo third fret

Intro

| Gmaj7 | G6 | | D/G | | G | | |

‖: Am   D   Bm   Em | C   F7   G   :‖

Verse 1

Gmaj7   G6
 The moon is right, the spirit's up,

D/G   G
 We're here tonight and that's enough.

Chorus 1

Am D Bm Em C   F7   G
Sim-ply having a wonderful Christmastime,

Am D Bm Em C   F7   G
Sim-ply having a wonderful Christmastime.

Verse 2

Gmaj7   G6
 The party's on, the feeling's here

D/G   G
 That only comes this time of year.

Chorus 2 As Chorus 1

Bridge 1

G   C   D   G
The choir of children sing their song,

Ding dong, ding dong,

    C   G Am G Am | G Am G Am |
Ding dong, ding, ohhhh.

Instrumental ‖: Gmaj7 | G6 | D/G | G :‖

Chorus 3
```
Am  D  Bm Em  C           F7        G
```
Sim-ply having a wonderful Christmastime,
```
Am  D  Bm Em  C           F7        G
```
Sim-ply having a wonderful Christmastime.

Verse 3
```
Gmaj7                G6
```
The word is out   about the town
```
D/G              G
```
To lift a glass,   ahhh, don't look down.

Chorus 4
```
Am  D  Bm Em  C           F7        G
```
Sim-ply having a wonderful Christmastime.

Bridge 2
```
G           C        D       G
```
The choir of children sing their song,
```
           C        D
```
They practise all year long.
```
     Am    G    Am
```
Ding dong, ding dong,
```
G    Am   G    Am
```
Ding dong, ding dong,
```
G    Am   G    D
```
Ding dong, ding dong.

Verse 4
```
Gmaj7                G6
```
The party's on,   the spirit's up,
```
D/G                G
```
We're here tonight   and that's enough.

Chorus 5   As Chorus 3

Verse 5
```
Gmaj7                G6
```
The moon is right,   the spirit's up,
```
D/G                G
```
We're here tonight   and that's enough.

Chorus 6   As Chorus 3

Outro | Gmaj7 C | Gmaj7 C | Gmaj7 C | Gmaj7 D | G ‖

Further Reading

If you've enjoyed this book why not check out some of the great titles below. They are available from all good music retailers and book shops, or you can visit our website: www.musicsales.com. In case of difficulty please contact Music Sales direct (see page 2).

The Chord Songbook Series

Play all your favourite hits with just a few easy chords for each song! The huge range of titles to choose from include:

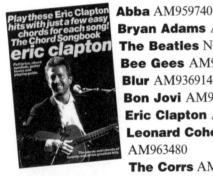

Abba AM959740
Bryan Adams AM963490
The Beatles NO90664
Bee Gees AM963556
Blur AM936914
Bon Jovi AM936892
Eric Clapton AM956054
Leonard Cohen AM963480
The Corrs AM956967
Dire Straits DG70834
Bob Dylan AM959706
The Jam AM958474
The Kinks AM956131
John Lennon AM956110
Bob Marley AM956109
Meat Loaf AM963534
Metallica AM944680
Elvis Presley AM956043
Paul Simon PS11485
Simon & Garfunkel PS11524
Stereophonics AM956065
Sting AM940489
Stone Roses AM951500
Travis AM963897
Paul Weller AM942546
The Who AM956021

Play Guitar With... Series

Play guitar and sing along with 'soundalike' CD backing tracks for classic songs from your favourite bands. Here are just some of the titles in this superb series:

The Beatles NO90665
Blues Legends AM958507
Bon Jovi AM92558
Eric Clapton AM950862
Eric Clapton Book 2 AM962896
Dire Straits DG70735
John Lee Hooker AM951885
B.B. King AM951874
The Kinks AM951863
John Lennon AM943756
Bob Marley AM937739
Metallica AM92559
Alanis Morissette AM943723
Oasis AM935330
Ocean Colour Scene AM943712
Paul Weller AM937827
Stereophonics AM960950
Sting AM928092
The Stone Roses AM943701

...plus many more
titles for you to collect!